Everyday Spelling

Third edition

Brown and Brown

Publishers: Brown and Brown,
Keeper's Cottage,
Westward,
Wigton
Cumbria CA7 8NQ
Tel. 016973 42915

First published 1989
Reprinted 1990
Second edition 1992
Reprinted 1994, 1997, 1999, 2001
Third edition 2001

ISBN 1 870596 83 8

Printed by Reed's Ltd., Penrith, Cumbria on 100% recycled paper and card.

Introduction

This workbook provides practice in some of the basics of spelling. It does not attempt to teach spelling techniques, although one or two useful tips are given.

Many of the words most commonly used in everyday reading and writing are included. Plenty of repetition is built into the workbook, and students should try to do each exercise without copying from other pages.

12 special practice pages deal with form-filling and words needed for writing cheques and letters. The practice pages should be followed in the order given in the book, but the exercises may be done in any order. In addition, there are 2 revision pages for each half of the book.

Third edition

For this **Third edition**, the text has been re-typeset and the samples used for form-filling practice have been updated where necessary.

Quite a number of minor alterations have been made to the text, so this edition should not be used alongside copies of previous editions.

---

*Other books in the **Everyday** series are:*

Everyday Cloze

ISBN 1 870596 28 5   *48 pages*

A book of 'cloze' exercises based on signs, notices and short items of everyday reading.

Everyday Maths

ISBN 1 870596 73 0   *48 pages*

A book of basic maths exercises covering maths problems in everyday situations.

Everyday Reading

ISBN 1 870596 74 9   *48 pages*

A book of short items of everyday reading matter, with exercises providing practice in basic reading skills.

For a complete catalogue of publications, please contact:

Brown and Brown, Keeper's Cottage, Westward, Wigton, Cumbria CA7 8NQ   *Tel. 016973 42915*

Contents

Name and address

Everyone needs to be able to spell their name and address. An address is often best learnt by the *Look - Say - Cover - Write - Check* method shown opposite.

- ○ Write your name, address and signature below.
- ○ Make sure that they are spelt correctly.
- ○ Use this page as a memory check when needed.

Use BLOCK CAPITALS

Name _____

Address _____

_____

_____

Use your usual handwriting

Name _____

Address _____

_____

_____

Signature _____

Look - Say - Cover - Write - Check

A basic way of learning to spell a word

1. Copy the word out in clear print. Don't use capital letters except where one is needed at the beginning of a word. *(Make sure the word is spelt correctly.)*

2. Read the word and say it. Look at the spelling of the word and notice any odd things about it. Count the number of letters in the word.

3. Close your eyes and try to picture it. Then look back at the word.

4. Cover the word up.

5. Write the word out in your usual handwriting.

6. Uncover the word and check your spelling against it.

7. If you have got it wrong, note the part that is wrong. Do Steps **2** to **7** again, covering up all the attempts you have made.

8. When you get it right, do it again at least twice to make sure you know it. Repeat it daily for at least a week.

This method can also be used for learning to spell short phrases and sentences or an address.

> **Note:** *This is only one of the many ways of learning to spell a word. Try out different methods, to find those which suit you best.*

Practice (1)

Fill in these extracts from everyday forms.

TELEVISION LICENCE

1 Your name and address

Title   **Initials**   **Surname**

Address

Post code

APPLICATION FOR A SUPPLY OF ELECTRICITY

1. WHAT IS YOUR NAME?

MR/MS/MRS . . . .
     SURNAME   FORENAMES

2. ADDRESS WHERE SUPPLY IS REQUIRED?

ADDRESS   . . . .
                . . . .
                POSTCODE . . . . TEL. NO. . . . .

Please complete and return to British Gas

Name ————————————————————————

Address ——————————————————————

————————————————————————

————————————————————————

Tel. No. (Home) ———————————————————

Tel. No. (Work) ————————————————————

Signed ———————————————— Date ——————

Key words (1)

Pick the right word to fill the gap in each sentence.

1. Do _____ forget to sign and date the form.
   (note / knot / not)

2. Give your surname and first name in _____ .
   (fall / full / fool)

3. When can you start _____ ?
   (work / walk / week)

4. For office _____ only.
   (us / used / use)

5. Fill in this _____ and send it to us as soon as you can.
   (from / form / farm)

6. You must sign the box above _____ your application to be considered.
   (for / four / fro)

7. I / We have _____ and agree to the conditions of sale.
   (red / reed / read)

8. Where do you _____ your bills sent to ?
   (wont / want / went)

9. Cheques should be made payable to _____ Office Counters Ltd.
   (Past / Pest / Post)

Key words (2)

Fill in the missing words in these notices.

1. Please do _____ smoke.

2. Beware of _____ bull.

3. No dogs allowed except _____ a leash.

4. DANGER ! Switch _____ when not in use.

5. Break glass in case of _____ .

6. Please _____ the door.

7. No parking in front _____ these gates.

8. Empty contents _____ a pan.

9. Ring bell _____ attention.

10. Please keep _____ the footpath.

11. Shoplifters _____ be prosecuted.

12. FIRE EXIT. _____ CLEAR.

13. All visitors _____ report to reception.

14. Please _____ your litter home.

15. Open at _____ end.

Key words (3)

One word is missing from each of these sentences and phrases.
Re-write them, putting in the missing words.

1. Thank for your letter.

2. Merry Christmas a Happy New Year.

3. We would to come to the wedding.

4. We were very to hear about Keith's death.

5. Your dinner in the oven.

6. Your brother rang say he can't make it.

7. Congratulations your Silver Wedding.

8. I enclose a cheque £20.

9. We're a lovely time here.

10. Can you me at the station at 7.30 p.m. ?

11. Simon will be off this week.

12. Further to letter of October 15th ......

13. We regret that we will not be to come to the Open Day.

14. Please my apologies at today's meeting.

Practice (2)

Fill in this extract from a Driving Licence Application.

Please write clearly in BLACK INK using CAPITAL LETTERS or tick ✓ the appropriate box.

1 Your details

Surname

Forename(s)

Mr ☐ Mrs ☐ Miss ☐ Ms ☐ Other title (e.g. Rev) ☐

Title Male ☐ Female ☐

	Day	Month	Year

Date of birth

What is your driver licence number? (if you have one)

☐☐☐☐☐ ☐☐☐☐☐ ☐☐☐☐☐

Address

Post Town Postcode

Place of birth (town or city)

Full daytime telephone number

Have you lived in another EC/EEA country in the last 12 months?

No ☐ Yes ☐

If yes, which country?

	Day	Month	Year

Date when you became resident in the U.K.

2 Your eyesight

Can you read a car number plate (with or without glasses or corrective lenses) from 20.5 metres (67 feet)? No ☐ Yes ☐

Key words (4)

Write a sentence which uses the words given in each line.

e.g	had	I	from
	I had come back late **from** the pub.		

1. and   only

2. at   he

3. some   said

4. a   them

5. be   see

6. are   that

7. but   is   then

8. were   so   all

9. in   been   if

10. as   they   you

11. have   this   old

12. two   him   about

13. she   your   with

14. the   not   on

Key words (5)

Across

1. Not second-hand (3)

5. Half of two (3)

7. "What time _____ you be home tonight?" (4)

9. "I did _____ my way." (2)

10. The traffic jam was 3 miles _____ . (4)

12. "We _____ to Spain last year." (4)

14. "Who does that woman think _____ is?" (3)

Down

1. It's _____ or never. (3)

2. Not ill (4)

3. Opposite of 'Stop' (2)

4. "Is the shop for sale or to _____ ?" (3)

6. The hours of darkness (5)

8. In tennis it means 'nil'. (4)

11. Neil Armstrong _____ the first man on the moon. (3)

12. "Where would _____ all be without him?" (2)

13. Opposite of 'Yes' (2)

Key words (6)

All these advertisements *did* appear in newspapers !

Fill in the missing key words.

A.

FOR SALE   Three piece suite.
Settee turns _____ bed covered
in thick yellow mustard.

B.

Ladies with elastic waist. Assortment of colours.
Under _____ - price.

C.

FOR SALE   Cottage piano, _____ in
Berlin. Owner getting grand.

D.

CLOTHES BRUSH   The genuine pigskin
back opens with a zipper, and _____ are
tweezers, scissors, nail-file and bomb.

E.

FOUND   White fox-terrier _____ . Apply
with name on collar to 51, Park Terrace, NW1.

F.

PLEASE NOTE
You can order rings _____ post. State size
or enclose string tied round finger.

Practice (3)

Fill in this extract from a Travel Insurance application.

1. Name and Address of first named person (Principal Insured)

Title (Mr/Mrs/Ms/Miss) Initials Surname   Date of Birth   Age

Address

House No: Road Name:

Town: County: Postcode:

Telephone:

2. Names of additional Person(s) to be Insured

Title (Mr/Mrs/Ms/Miss) Initials Surname   Date of Birth   Age

3. Single Trip Cover (max. 90 day trip)

Departure Date   Return Date

No. of days   Country of Destination

(Inclusive of date of departure and date of return)

Travel Insurance *(please tick appropriate boxes)*

☐ Individual Cover   ☐ Couple Cover   ☐ Family Cover

☐ Single Parent Family   ☐ Ski/Winter Sport Cover

Area   ☐ UK   ☐ Europe   ☐ Worldwide

b / d (1)

b and d are often confused in spelling and reading.

One way to remember which is which is to think of the word **bed**. If **bed** is spelt correctly, it looks like a bed seen from the side:

bed = bed

If it is spelt wrongly (*e.g.* deb, beb *or* ded), it doesn't look like a bed.

If you are not sure whether to write **b** or **d** when spelling a word, say the word aloud and then compare the **b** or **d** sound with the sounds in **bed**.

In each line, pick out the word or words on the right which are spelt the same way as the word on the left.

bed	bad	dab	deb	bed	bud
did	dub	did	dib	bid	bib
bud	but	bud	dub	dud	bed
band	bend	bind	band	drab	bard
debt	debit	debt	dept	debt	deep
BREAD	dread	BRED	breed	bread	bread
dead	BEAD	dead	DEED	dread	DEAD
double	double	doodle	bubble	doubt	double

b / d (2)

1. *How many of these words contain the letter 'b' ?*
   Underline every letter 'b'.

back	danger	about	downstairs
road	bridge	cold	basement
bar	before	because	pedestrians

2. *How many of these words contain the letter 'd' ?*
   Underline every letter 'd'.

brother	closed	door	engaged
address	beware	said	bottom
ladies	did	been	underpass

3. *Fill in 'b' and 'd' in these place-names:*

Car__iff	E__in__urgh	__u__lin
__er__y	__un__ee	A__er__een
__urham	__irmingham	Lon__on
__ra__for__	Llan__u__no	__elfast

b / d (3)

Underline all the 'b's and 'd's in this piece.
Which letter appears most often - 'b' or 'd' ?

The Wrong Label

In October 1971, a 9-year-old girl, Fiona Gordon, went to look round a museum at South Shields on Tyneside. She saw an object which had a label on it saying it was a Roman coin made between 135 AD and 138 AD. She pointed out that it was not a 2000-year-old Roman coin but a plastic token given away free by a soft drinks firm. A spokesman for the Roman Fort Museum said the token had been made to look like a Roman coin. They had thought that the *R* on the coin stood for *Roman,* but it really stood for *Robinson's,* the soft drinks firm !

A writing tip

When writing the small **b**, think of the capital **B** first. Write the **b** as a capital letter, but don't touch the paper with the pen as you write the top loop.

e.g. **b b b**

Practice (4)

Fill in this extract from an Income Support claim form.

About you

National Insurance (NI) number

Letters   Numbers   Letter

Surname or family name

Mr / Mrs / Miss / Ms

All other names in full

All other surnames or family names you have been known by or are using now.

Date of birth   /   /

Address

Postcode

Daytime phone number   Code   Number

Textphone number   Code   Number

Children you want to claim for

Surname	Other names	Date of birth	Relationship to you e.g. son, niece, none
		/ /	
		/ /	
		/ /	

b / d (4)

1. **Fill in the missing letters ('b' or 'd') in this joke from Morecambe and Wise:**

   ERIC: See that __eautiful __lon__e over there ?

   ERNIE: Yes !

   ERIC: She's __een annoying me all evening.

   ERNIE: I __et she hasn't even looke__ at you !

   ERIC: Right - that's what's __een annoying me !

2. **Fill in the missing letters ('b' or 'd') in these notices:**

   __ANGER
   ROA__ WORKS
   AHEA__

   __EWARE
   __uring the hours of __arkness
   these premises are patrolle__ __y
   GUAR__ __OGS

Question words (1)

A. There are seven words which are often used for asking questions. Six of them begin with **wh** and one with **h**.

Fill in the gaps:

wh___   wh___   wh___ ___

wh___ ___   wh___ ___ ___ wh___ ___ ___

h___ ___

B. *Put a different question word into each sentence.*

1. _____ do you have to see the doctor again ?

2. _____ do you think she can have got to ?

3. _____ much did you pay for it ?

4. _____ was the man I saw you with last night ?

5. _____ are we waiting ?

6. _____ way is it to the Bus Station, please ?

7. _____ time is it ?

C. *Which two question words begin with an 'h' sound ?*
(as in 'hospital')

D. *With which sound do the other five question words begin ?*

Question words (2)

A. Here are the answers to some questions.

Write down a question for each answer.

1. "I have been waiting for over half an hour."

2. "I bought it in a sale last week."

3. "She's the old lady who lives in the top flat."

4. "She rang about half an hour ago."

5. "The man standing in the back row with a bald head and glasses."

6. "It's a beat-up old Volvo Estate."

7. "It's the room with the red door, just along the corridor."

8. "Because I'm going to Wrexham tomorrow."

9. "They're £1 for five, or 25p each."

10. "It fell off the back of a lorry, officer."

B. Make up seven questions of your own, using each of the question words from page 22.

Practice (5)

Fill in this extract from a Loan Application Form

Name and Address of applicant

(Mr/Mrs/Miss/Ms) Surname

Present address

Postcode

Home telephone number _____ Date of birth

Address occupied as Owner/Tenant/With parents/Other

Type of residence: House ☐ Bungalow ☐ Flat ☐ Other ☐

How long at present address?

Previous address

Postcode

How long at previous address?

Employment details: Employer's name

Address

Occupation type: Unemployed ☐ Retired ☐ Unskilled ☐

Clerical/Other ☐ Housewife/Homemaker ☐ Professional ☐

Director ☐ Senior M'ment ☐ Middle M'ment ☐ Student ☐

Skilled craftsperson ☐ Armed forces ☐ Self employed ☐

Job title _____ How long in present job?

Vowels (1)

1. The two most common sounds for each of the five vowels are given in the boxes below.

    Two examples are given for each sound.
    Add at least 2 more of your own.

	Short sound		Long sound	
a	avenue	back	April	station
e	exit	chemist	evening	she
i	into	drink	idea	drive
o	office	coffee	only	local
u	under	Sunday	union	June

2. *Which of the above sounds are in your name and address ?*

Vowels (2)

1. **Which of these words have a long 'a' sound in them, and which have a short 'a' sound ?**

   place   woman   fragile   information

   ladies   have   ace   afternoon

2. **Which of these words have a long 'e' sound in them, and which have a short 'e' sound ?**

   west   people   engaged   television

   legal   event   wedding   premium

3. **Which of these words have a long 'i' sound in them, and which have a short 'i' sound ?**

   write   lifts   diet   written

   inside   wife   private   dinner

4. **Which of these words have a long 'o' sound in them, and which have a short 'o' sound ?**

   only   office   post   overhead

   cold   stop   closing   hospital

5. **Which of these words have a long 'u' sound in them, and which have a short 'u' sound ?**

   union   until   United   avenue

   July   umpire   student   unemployed

Note: Some words may have both long and short vowels in them.

Vowels (3)

Fill in the vowels in this newspaper item.

BANK RAID FAILS

In 1969, __t Portland in the U.S.A., a m__n w__nt into a bank to r__b it. He d__d not want to cause any p__nic, so he s__t down to wr__te a note. It said, "Th__s is a hold-up and I've g__t a g__n."

H__ went to the d__sk and held the note __p for the b__nk clerk to read. The bank clerk th__n waited __s the robber wr__te, "P__t all the money in a p__per bag."

He p__shed this n__te through the grille. The bank clerk read it __nd then wrote __n the b__ttom, "I do n__t have a paper b__g," and p__ssed it b__ck.

The r__bber fl__d.

Practice (6)

Fill in this High Street Store Points Card Application

Please use BLOCK CAPITALS when completing this form

Your title

Your first name

Your surname

Address

Town

County

Postcode

Your email address (for details of products, offers and services)

Your mobile phone number (for text messages of product offers)

How many people in your family live at the above address?

If you have any children under sixteen, what are their dates of birth?

If you are pregnant, when is the baby due?

Do you wear? Spectacles Contact Lenses Both None

Date of your last eye test

Vowels (4)

1.   Fill in each gap with a vowel to make a word, as shown.

	a	e	i	o	u
p - n	pan	pen	pin	-	pun
- n					
t - p					
s - t					
r - m					
b - d					
l - d					
l - st					
b - nd					
m - ss					

2.   How many words can you make by adding one letter in front of each of these ?

(*e.g.* **-ace** : **d**ace, **f**ace, **l**ace, **m**ace, **p**ace, **r**ace)

-ame   -ave   -eed   -ole   -ue

-iner   -ower   -ight   -ating   -otion

Vowels (5)

The letter **y** is sometimes a vowel and sometimes a consonant. It is usually a vowel when it is in the middle or at the end of a word.

1. In the box below are examples of the 2 sounds of **y** when it is a vowel.

    Add at least two more words to each list.

'y' as a vowel	
'y' *as in* **'by'** (sounds like long 'i')	**'y'** *as in* **'very'** (sounds like long 'e')
July dry	February many

2. *Which of these words has a 'y' which sounds like long 'i' ?* *(as in 'my')*

    by   spy   marry   putty   why   sorry   apply

3. *Which of these words has a 'y' which sounds like long 'e' ?* *(as in 'twenty')*

    any   shy   carrying   trying   January   tidy

Vowels (6)

1.   *Fill each gap with a word from the box.*

money	other	brother	some	does
above	month	doesn't	Monday	come
done	wonder	son	mother	

On the first _____ of each _____ , all our
family meets for a night-out together. We've _____
it for years now - ever since Dad died. It's often the only time
my _____ sees the whole lot of us all at once.

Everyone tries to _____ if they can, but my younger
_____ , Joe, works shifts and he _____
always make it.   My _____ brother has three
daughters and a _____ , and _____ of
them are usually there.

Mum only has her pension now, so she's often a bit short of
_____ , but she keeps her head _____
water somehow. She _____ get a few pounds from
my Dad's firm, but I _____ how she manages to get
by these days.

2.   *What do the words in the box have in common ?*

1. **Write down the 7 question words that rhyme with these words:**

   pie   do

   hot   ten

   hair   rich

   now

2. **Fill in the blanks in this postcard and address it to someone you know or to your own home.**

___day   *POST CARD*   POST OFFICE
                                       PREFERRED

Having a great ___.
Went to Loch Ness ___.
Going on to Oban ___.
The weather's been fine.
___ says it always rains
in Scotland? Wish we
were ___ for the rest
of the ___. The boys
don't ___ to go home.
    Love _____

River Spey   Feshie Bridge   Aviemore
Old Carr Bridge   Loch Insh   Nethybridge

3. *Fill in the missing letters ('b' or 'd'):*

> ___o something amazing to___ay.
>
> ## GIVE ___LOO___ !
>
> New ___onors must ___e age___ ___etween 17 an___ 60, weigh more than 7st 12 l___s (50kg) an___ ___e in goo___ health.
>
> We nee___ just un___er a pint of ___loo___ and a___out an hour of your time. You shoul___ ___e feeling well on the ___ay an___ have ha___ something to eat an___ ___rink ___eforehan___ . After ___onation, you rest on the ___e___ for a___out 10 minutes, then we give you a ___rink an___ a ___iscuit. Your goo___ ___ee___ coul___ save a life. ___o it to___ay!
>
> *To fin___ your nearest ___onation centre, phone 0845 7 711 711 or visit our we___site at www.___loo___.co.uk.*

4. *Put vowels into each of these pairs of words to make 2 different words:*

(*e.g.* l___d   l___d = lid   lad)

1. p___t	p___t	**5.** p___st	p___st
2. m___t	m___t	**6.** ch___p	ch___p
3. b___g	b___g	**7.** s___ck	s___ck
4. m___	m___	**8.** f___ll	f___ll

Put each word into a sentence to show its meaning.

Days and Months (1)

A. *Write down the day of the week which is:*

1. The first day of the working week.

2. The day when the Grand National is run.

3. Pancake day.

4. The middle of the week.

5. The day of rest.

6. The day when U.K. elections are held.

7. The first of the two Easter Bank Holidays.

B. *Write down the word which is used for:*

1. This day.

2. The day after this day.

3. The day before this day.

4. 7 days.

5. 14 days.

6. 30 or 31 days.

7. 365 or 366 days.

8. The last two days of the week.

Days and Months (2)

A. Write down the month which:

1. Has only 3 letters in its name.

2. Has Bonfire Night on the 5th.

3. Is when the school summer holidays start.

4. Sounds like an army walking.

5. Is the last month of the year.

6. Has the last U.K. Bank Holiday before Christmas.

7. Is the first month of the year.

8. Has a Fools' Day.

9. Is when the clocks go back.

10. Has only 28 or 29 days in it.

11. Is when the English cricket season ends.

12. Has the longest day in it.

B. Write down the names of the four seasons.

Practice (7)

A. *Fill in the missing letters* (Days, Months and Numbers).

Mon _ _ _	Jan _ _ _ _	o _ e	1
Tue _ _ _ _	Feb _ _ _ _ _	t _ o	2
Wed _ _ _ _ _ _	Mar _ _	thr _ _	3
Thu _ _ _ _ _	Apr _ _	f _ _ r	4
Fri _ _ _	M _ _	f _ _ e	5
Sat _ _ _ _ _	Jun _	s _ x	6
Sun _ _ _	Jul _	s _ _ _ n	7
	Aug _ _ _	e _ _ _ t	8
yes _ _ _ _ _ _	Sept _ _ _ _ _	n _ _ e	9
to _ _ _	Oct _ _ _ _	t _ n	10
to _ _ _ _ _ _	Nov _ _ _ _ _	e _ _ _ _ n	11
hol _ _ _ _	Dec _ _ _ _ _	t _ _ _ _ e	12

B. *Fill in the missing letters* (Greetings from letters and cards).

D _ _ r   S _ r   _ r   M _ d _ m

Y _ _ rs   s _ nc _ r _ ly

Y _ _ rs   f _ _ thf _ lly

W _ th   b _ st   w _ sh _ s

H _ ppy   B _ rthd _ y

36

Numbers (1)

A. *Write the answers to these in words:*

2	+	3	=	4	+	3	=
11	+	6	=	14	-	3	=
11	-	8	=	19	-	18	=
9	-	7	=	7	+	7	=
2	+	4	=	9	-	5	=
8	+	4	=	19	-	11	=
21	-	6	=	9	+	4	=
11	+	8	=	24	-	6	=
10	x	2	=	20	x	2	=
60	+	40	=	85	+	5	=
41	-	11	=	18	÷	2	=
60	-	50	=	8	x	2	=
25	+	25	=	41	+	19	=
86	-	16	=	20	x	4	=
101	-	101	=	999	+	1	=

B. *Write each line of numbers as words:*

5	15	50
4	14	40

Which spelling in each line is the odd one out ?
Explain why.

Numbers (2)

A. Which numbers between 1 and 20 are spelt with 3 letters each ?

B. Which 4 letters come at the end of all numbers from 13 to 19 ?

C. Which 2 letters are in all numbers from 20 to 99 ?

D. Which numbers between 1 and 20 begin with 't' ?

E. Write these as words:

1st	2nd	3rd	4th	5th
6th	7th	8th	9th	10th

F. Which other words can be used for these numbers ?

(*e.g.* **a** for **one** : She took **a** *(one)* bite.)

one	two	three	four

G. What number is:

a dozen ?	a century ?
a grand ?	a ream ?
a sextet ?	10 k ?

H. Write these as words:

$1/2$ $1/3$ $1/4$ $1/5$ $1/6$ $1/7$ $1/8$ $1/9$

Numbers (3)

A. How many ?

Fill in the missing numbers in words.

1. _____ inches in a foot.

2. _____ millimetres in a centimetre.

3. _____ feet in a yard.

4. _____ grams in a kilogram.

5. _____ ounces in a pound.

6. _____ pence in a pound.

7. _____ seconds in a minute.

8. _____ minutes in half an hour.

9. _____ pints in a gallon.

B. Fill in the missing numbers (in words):

1. _____'s company, _____'s a crowd.

2. _____ of one, half a dozen of the other.

3. A cat has _____ lives.

4. The _____ days of Christmas.

5. She's in _____ heaven.

6. He's had one over the _____ .

7. The car has _____-wheel drive.

8. She's _____ in a million.

9. _____pin bowling.

Practice (8)

A. Fill in the missing letters *(Days, Months and Numbers).*

M _ _ day	_ _ _ uary	_ _ _	1
T _ _ _ day	_ _ _ ruary	_ _ _	2
W _ _ _ _ _ day	_ _ _ ch	_ _ _ _ _	3
T _ _ _ _ day	_ _ _ il	_ _ _ _	4
F _ _ day	_ ay	_ _ _ _	5
S _ _ _ _ day	_ _ _ e	_ _ _	6
S _ _ day	_ _ _ y	_ _ _ _ _	7
	_ _ _ ust	_ _ _ _ _	8
y _ _ _ _ _ day	_ _ _ _ ember	_ _ _ _	9
t _ day	_ _ _ ober	_ _ _	10
t _ morrow	_ _ _ ember	_ _ _ _ _ _	11
h _ _ _ day	_ _ _ ember	_ _ _ _ _ _	12

B. Fill in the missing letters *(Greetings from letters and cards).*

_ ea _   _ i _   o _   _ a _ a _

_ ou_ _   _ i _ _ e _ e _y

_ ou_ _   _ ai _ _ _ u _ _ y

_ i _ _   _ e_ _   _ i _ _ e _

_ a _ _ y   _ i _ _ _ _ ay

40

Cheques

Write out cheques for the amounts given.

Make the cheques payable to local shops, suppliers or organisations, where possible.

Electricity bill	£92.42
Telephone bill	£84.78
Monthly Council Tax	£73.50
Insurance Company	£62.27
Supermarket	£36.74
High Street store	£19.99
Withdrawal of money	£40.00
Monthly rent / Mortgage	£235.61
Petrol	£18.60
Mail order firm	£57.85
Television licence	£104.00
Donation to Charity	£15.00
Tickets for a show / sports event	£31.00
Meal in a restaurant	£28.32

Note: *An A4 sheet of blank cheques for practice is supplied with this book. The sheet may be photocopied as required.*

Silent letters (1)

In some of these sentences, the silent **e** ending is used wrongly or is missing.

Correct the mistakes.

1. "I wish I was slime."

2. Acid rain is killing a lot of pin trees.

3. "I can't cope with the in-laws at Christmas."

4. The quickest way from Kings Cross to Victoria is by tub.

5. She set fir to the fire tree.

6. The U.S. flag is called the Stars and Stripes.

7. "Well, I think it is a case of use or them."

8. Marion Jones was the first to reach the tap.

9. The Land Rover used 4-wheel drive to get up the slope.

10. "Where did you get that hate ?"

11. "These bananas are not rip."

12. A man was killed today on a city building site.

13. The letter was lying on the door mat.

14. Please drive with car.

Silent letters (2)

Read the conversation below, then try to carry on writing it using silent 'e' words in the same way.

Silent 'e' at the Council Offices

Jane   Hello, Karen.

Karen   Hello, Jan.

Jane   No, I'm Jane. Don't you remember ?

Karen   Isn't your baby cut ?

Jane   Oh, my God ! Where ?

Karen   No, no ! It's got a cut face.

Jane   You mean cute.

Karen   Mind you, he does look a little pal.

Jane   Yes, he is, but he's off colour today and very pale.

Karen   Yes. Have you been paying the rats ?

Jane   No, I've been to pay the rates.

Karen   Oh, yes. I'm going to the repairs office. I smashed a pan this morning.

Jane   Can you get a new pan on the rates ?

Karen   Yes. They have to repair broken windows, if you can get through all the red tap. I've been waiting three months for them to mend the broken downpip. I've just about given up hop. Sometimes I think they keep you waiting out of spit !

Practice (9)

A. Fill in the missing letters *(Days, Months and Numbers).*

M _ nd _ y	J _ n _ _ ry	t _ _ _ _ _ _ n	13
T _ _ sd _ y	F _ br _ _ ry	f _ _ _ _ _ _ n	14
W _ dn _ sd _ y	M _ rch	f _ _ _ _ _ n	15
Th _ rsd _ y	_ pr _ l	s _ _ _ _ _ n	16
Fr _ d _ y	M _ y	s _ _ _ _ _ _ _ n	17
S _ t _ rd _ y	J _ n _	e _ _ _ _ _ _ n	18
S _ nd _ y	J _ ly	n _ _ _ _ _ _ n	19
	_ _ g _ st	t _ _ _ _ y	20
y _ st _ rd _ y	S _ pt _ mb _ r	t _ _ _ _ y	30
t _ d _ y	_ ct _ b _ r	f _ _ _ y	40
t _ m _ rr _ w	N _ v _ mb _ r	f _ _ _ y	50
h _ l _ d _ y	D _ c _ mb _ r	s _ _ _ y	60

B. Fill in the missing letters *(Greetings from letters and cards).*

D _ _ _   S _ _

Your _   sincere _ _

Your _   faithful _ _

W _ _ h   b _ _ t   w _ _ _ _ s

H _ _ _ y   B _ _ _ _ _ _ y

Silent letters (3)

A. *Fill in the missing silent letters.*

1. Spring, Summer, Autum___ , Winter

2. ___nife and fork

3. Fingers and thum___s

4. Ri___ ___ t and ___rong

5. Roast lam___ and mint sauce

6. Hi___ ___ and low

7. Hands and ___nees

8. Ni___ ___t and day

B. *Fill in the missing words.*
Each word contains at least one silent letter.

1. Please _____ and enter.

2. " _____ goes there ?"

3. "He _____ have seen the doctor weeks ago."

4. _____ your name on the dotted line.

5. She took the dog for a _____ every day.

6. Please _____ in block capitals.

Silent letters (4)

All the answers in the puzzle contain the same silent letter.

Across

3. Cold and without feeling (4)
5. Something owed (*e.g.* money) (4)
6. Go up a mountain (5)
7. Person who mends pipes (7)
8. A burial place (4)
9. A deadly weapon (4)

Down

1. Unable to speak (4)
2. Brush and _____ (4)
4. An arm or leg (4)
5. To be unsure (5)
6. A tiny piece of bread (5)

Answers on p.63

Silent letters (5)

A. *Re-write this letter, putting in the silent letters the writer has left out.*

> 12, Blackwood Driv,
> Stok-on-Trent
> Jun 1st 2001
>
> Dear Bill,
>
> Thank you for your letter, wich cam today. I'm riting to say that I woud lik to com to your party on Wensday nit.
>
> Coud you let me now how to get ther ? It's a long tim since I hav been to your hous and I don't want to take the rong road from the station.
>
> Is it all rit if I bring my new girlfrend with me ?
>
> Yours,
>
> Joe

B. *Write a letter or a short story which contains all these words:*

fright	sight	thought	weight	ought
tight	caught	eight	might	neighbour

Practice (10)

A.   Fill in the missing letters *(Days, Months and Numbers).*

_ o _ _ a _	_ a _ ua _ _	_ _ _ _ _ _ _ _ _ 13
_ ue _ _ a _	_ e _ _ ua _ _	_ _ _ _ _ _ _ _ _ 14
_ e _ _ e _ _ a _	_ a _ _ _	_ _ _ _ _ _ _ 15
_ _ u _ _ _ a _	A _ _ i _	_ _ _ _ _ _ _ 16
_ _ i _ a _	_ a _	_ _ _ _ _ _ _ _ _ 17
_ a _ u _ _ a _	_ u _ e	_ _ _ _ _ _ _ 18
_ u _ _ a _	_ u _ _	_ _ _ _ _ _ _ _ _ 19
	Au _ u _ _	_ _ _ _ _ _ 20
_ e _ _ e _ _ a _	_ e _ _ e _ _ e _	_ _ _ _ _ _ 30
_ o _ a _	O _ _ o _ e _	_ _ _ _ _ 40
_ o _ o _ _ o _	_ o _ e _ _ e _	_ _ _ _ _ 50
_ o _ i _ a _	_ e _ e _ _ e _	_ _ _ _ _ 60

B.   Fill in the missing letters *(Greetings from letters and cards).*

D _ _ _   M _ _ _ _

Y _ _ _ _   since _ _ _ _

Y _ _ _ _   faith _ _ _ _ _

W _ _ _   b _ _ _   w _ _ _ _ _

H _ _ _ _   B _ _ _ _ _ _ _

48

Notes and Messages

Finish these notes and messages, adding names where they are needed.

1. Gone to ....

2. I have left the ....

3. MILKMAN. Please leave ....

4. Don't forget to ....

5. DANGER ! Do not ....

6. Sorry I forgot to ....

7. Mr. Singh rang. Could you ....

8. Your dinner is ....

9. The car has ....

10. Can you pick up ....

11. WET PAINT ON ....

12. PLUMBER. Mrs. Jones, at number 10, has ....

13. I can't find the ....

14. I called round today but ....

15. The builders have ....

16. I found this ....

c / g (1)

When **c** is followed by **e**, **i** or **y**, it usually sounds like **s**.

When **g** is followed by **e**, **i** or **y**, it usually sounds like **j**.

Fill in the blanks in these signs.

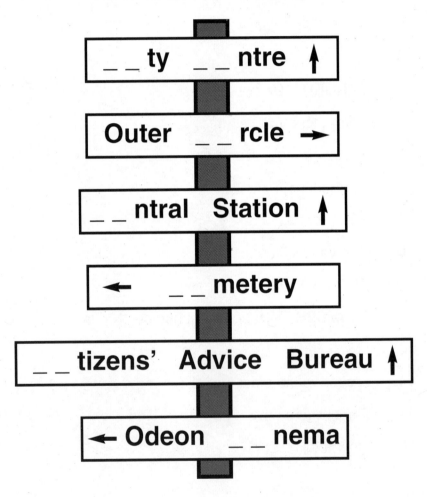

_ _ ty _ _ ntre ↑

Outer _ _ rcle →

_ _ ntral Station ↑

← _ _ metery

_ _ tizens' Advice Bureau ↑

← Odeon _ _ nema

c / g (2)

A. All the answers in the puzzle begin with **ge**, **gi** or **gy**.

Ladies and _____

A hot spice

A traveller

A bug

Place for weight training

_____ and tonic

Unemployment benefit cheque

Soft and kind

B. All the answers in the puzzle begin with **ce**, **ci** or **cy**.

Eat it for breakfast

Greek / Turkish island

Powder used in concrete

Drink made from apples

Spot or blister

A prisoner's room

Causes lung cancer

Cold water tank

Answers on p.63

Practice (11)

A. *Fill in the missing letters* (Days, Months and Numbers).

M _ _ _ _ y	J _ _ _ _ _ y	s _ _ _ _ _ y	70
T _ _ _ _ _ y	F _ _ _ _ _ _ y	e _ _ _ _ y	80
W _ _ _ _ _ _ _ _ y	M _ _ _ h	n _ _ _ _ y	90
T _ _ _ _ _ _ y	A _ _ _ l	h _ _ _ _ _ _ d	100
F _ _ _ _ y	M _ y	t _ _ _ _ _ _ d	1000
S _ _ _ _ _ _ y	J _ _ e	m _ _ _ _ _ _ n	1,000,000
S _ _ _ _ y	J _ _ y	e _ _ _ t	8
	A _ _ _ _ t	e _ _ _ _ n	11
y _ _ _ _ _ _ _ y	S _ _ _ _ _ _ _ r	t _ _ _ e	12
t _ _ _ y	O _ _ _ _ _ r	f _ _ y	40
t _ _ _ _ _ _ w	N _ _ _ _ _ _ r	p _ _ _ _ s	£
h _ _ _ _ _ y	D _ _ _ _ _ _ r	p _ _ e	p

B. *Fill in the missing letters* (Greetings from letters and cards).

D _ _ _   M _   and   M _ _

Y _ _ _ _   s _ _ _ _ _ _ _

Y _ _ _   f _ _ _ _ _ _ _ _

W _ _ _   b _ _ _   w _ _ _ _ _

H _ _ _ _   B _ _ _ _ _ _

Alphabet (1)

1. **How many letters are there in the alphabet ?**

   24   26   28

2. **In the alphabet, where does each of these letters come** *(roughly)* **- at the beginning, in the middle or near the end ?**

d	w	m	y	j	c
p	b	l	o	v	x

3. Open a dictionary halfway through.

   What is the first letter of the words on that page ?

4. **What is the first letter of the words on a page a quarter of the way through the dictionary ?**

5. **What is the first letter of the words on a page three quarters of the way through the dictionary ?**

6. **Fill in the gaps:**

   c d __ f   s __ u v   l m __ o

7. **What letter comes after each of these in the alphabet ?**

   h   y   b   r   j   q

8. **What letter comes before each of these in the alphabet ?**

   l   b   h   p   i   u

Alphabet (2)

A. *Put these letters into alphabetical order:*

1.   t   f   e   p   c

2.   r   v   x   s   q

B. *Which word in each pair comes first in alphabetical order ?*
Underline the letter which decides the order

     e.g.   ch<u>e</u>ese (1)   ch<u>o</u>colate (2)

1.	fish	eggs
2.	rice	potatoes
3.	tea	biscuits
4.	beans	flour
5.	sugar	sherry
6.	margarine	marmalade
7.	peas	peaches
8.	soup	soap
9.	cake	carrots
10.	cornflakes	cornflour

Alphabet (3)

A. Put these places into alphabetical order:

Norwich	Inverness	Hereford	Ballymena
Perth	Preston	Glasgow	Brighton
Newport	Bangor	Carlisle	Northampton

B. Now try these:

Sheffield	Strabane	Southampton
Stirling	Swansea	Sunderland
Southport	Shrewsbury	Stornoway

C. In a dictionary, which of the words in each line would come first ? Underline it.

1. repeat   replace   renew   reminder

2. pay   pound   pence   postage   profit

3. informal   inform   informer   information

4. schooling   scheme   school   schedule

5. trailer   trainer   tray   traitor   train

Practice (12)

A. Fill in the missing letters *(Days, Months and Numbers).*

M _____	J _____	_ _ _ _ _ _ _ _ 70
T _____	F _____	_ _ _ _ _ _ 80
W _____	M _____	_ _ _ _ _ _ 90
T _____	A _____	_ _ _ _ _ _ _ 100
F _____	M _____	_ _ _ _ _ _ _ _ 1000
S _____	J _____	_ _ _ _ _ _ _ _ 1,000,000
S _____	J _____	_ _ _ _ _ 8
	A _____	_ _ _ _ _ _ 11
y _____	S _____	_ _ _ _ _ _ 12
t _____	O _____	_ _ _ _ 40
t _____	N _____	_ _ _ _ _ £
h _____	D _____	_ _ _ _ _ p

B. Fill in the missing letters *(Greetings from letters and cards).*

Dear _____

Y_____   s_____

Y_____   f_____

W_____   b_____   w_____

H_____   B_____

Double letters (1)

A. *Fill in the right word.*

Saying each word aloud will help you to choose the right one.

A Night Out

Craig _____ *(taped / tapped)* his fingers nervously on the bar. He was having a pint of _____ *(biter / bitter)* while he waited for his date to arrive.

He had been _____ *(planing / planning)* for this night all week. He was taking his boss to a rock concert _____ *(starring / staring)* her favourite band and then, _____ *(later / latter)*, they were going to have _____ *(diner / dinner)* at a Greek restaurant.

Craig was only a _____ *(filling / filing)* clerk at the moment, but there was a better job coming up in the office next week. He _____ *(hopped / hoped)* that _____ *(wining / winning)* and dining the boss would give him a chance to find out how highly she _____ *(ratted / rated)* him.

B. *Make a list of the words which you did not use to fill the gaps in section A.*

Use each word in a sentence to show its meaning.

Double letters (2)

A. Fill the gaps with single or double letters.

Paul Jackson had two medals for swi____ing and he was ho____ing that he would get another one in the men's 100m Bu____erfly that night.

He was begi____ing to wish he was feeling fi____er. He really ha____ed training, but he was ge____ing be____er at it since leaving school because he had more time to practise. He had been dro____ed from the team last year, but that didn't ma____er now that he had been picked for tonight's big event.

As he stri____ed off and ste____ed over to the edge of the pool, he prayed that he wouldn't be pi____ed at the post and sto____ed from wi____ing.

B. All these jumbled words have double letters in them. Sort them out.

TRUBET   POSHPING   DESTOPT   PUSREP

TERTLE   SPILGLEN   TINTGINK   TEFTID

*Answers to **B**. on p.63*

Punctuation (1)

A. **Write these words in their short form, using a full stop to show that they are shortened.**

        e.g.   Road = Rd.

Saint	Street
Mister	Reverend
Doctor	Avenue
Mistress	Square
Drive	Telephone

B. **Write out these abbreviations in full.**

Look them up in a dictionary if you are not sure.

p.t.o.	e.g.	R.S.V.P
P.S.	o.n.o.	etc.
a.s.a.p.	M.P.	n.b. (*or* N.B.)
R.I.P.	O.K.	No.
P.O.	a.m.	p.m.

Punctuation (2)

A. *Re-write this advertisement, putting in full stops, capital letters and commas where they are needed.*

---

for sale

blue three piece suite black and decker drill hoover twin tub washing machine philips electric shaver good as new owner going abroad £100 ono tel 32034

B. *Re-write this poster, putting in full stops, capital letters and commas where they are needed.*

town green mothers and toddlers group

christmas fair

a christmas fair will be held

at town green community centre

on saturday 5th december at 2pm

it will be opened by the lord mayor mrs joan wheeler

all the money will go to the save the children fund

please come and bring your friends

raffle with super prizes

Punctuation (3)

A. *Put an apostrophe (') into each of the words in bold print.*

Bob **OConnor didnt** feel well. He came home from work early, but his wife **wasnt** in. She had left a note on the kitchen table:

> **Wont** be home till 9 **oclock**. **Theres** fish pie in the freezer, but if you **dont** fancy that **well** have a takeaway when I get home.

Bob **wasnt** hungry. He **didnt** think he could eat anything at all. So he left another note:

> Gone to bed. **Dont** feel well. **Wont** have any supper. Hope **its** not flu.

B. *Write out this conversation in full, as shown.*

"What's the time ?"   *"What is the time ?"*

"It's 10 o'clock."

"I didn't think it was so late."

"I can't finish this tonight."

"Let's go to the pub."

"That's a good idea."

Revision (2)

A. *Write a note or message which ends with each of these phrases:*

1. .... 3 o'clock today.

2. .... in the oven.

3. .... needs mending.

4. .... to the hospital.

5. .... when you get home.

6. .... when I get home.

7. .... tomorrow morning.

8. .... and a loaf of bread.

9. .... pints today, please.

10. .... gone missing.

B. *Write out the following in alphabetical order:*

1. The days of the week.

2. The months of the year.

3. Numbers 1 -10 *(in words).*

Revision (2)

Re-write this letter, filling in the blanks and putting in capital letters, full stops and commas where they are needed.

26 church lan__

bri__ __ton

feb__ __ary 3rd 20__ __

dear mr smith

i am __riting to let you __now that kelly will not be in school this week she has a bad cold and cou__h and the doctor says she shou__d stay in bed

yours sincer__ly

(mrs) jean jones

Index